BOOK... TRUST ME!

TUNDRA II

MORE Cartoons From the Last Frontier

By

Chad Carpenter

Chad Carpenter

Published by
𝕿𝖔𝖉𝖉 𝕮𝖔𝖒𝖒𝖚𝖓𝖎𝖈𝖆𝖙𝖎𝖔𝖓𝖘
203 W. 15th Ave. Suite 102
Anchorage, Alaska 99501 U. S. A.
(907) 274-8633   Fax (907) 276-6858

TUNDRA II – MORE Cartoons From The Last Frontier
By Chad Carpenter

Please mail US$13 in the U. S. or US$16 outside U. S. (includes postage and handling) for each additional copy of *TUNDRA II – MORE Cartoons from the Last Frontier* to:

Todd Communicaitons

203 W. 15th Ave. Suite 102
Anchorage, Alaska 99501
United States
(907) 274-8633   FAX (907) 276-6858

Also available at the above prices: TUNDRA © 1993, Chad Carpenter's first book of cartoons.

Wholesale quantities also available.

First Printing: April 1994
ISBN 1-878100-55-6
Printed in the United States of America

I dedicate my second book to
my brother, Darin Carpenter
(because he wasn't mentioned in the first one).

A few words from Mike Peters,
the creator of *Mother Goose & Grimm:*

TUNDRA is what "Northern Exposure" would be if it were a comic strip. This is all virgin territory for the cartoon field. How refreshing it is to explore the last wild American frontier and laugh at the same time. Crazy Chad is funny! Dudley the Bear is funny and Sherman the Squirrel is funny! We thought cartoonists like Chad Carpenter were extinct. But lo! – out of the North comes a really new idea – as surprising and unexpected as the aurora borealis. Luckily, the Tundra is vast and Chad will never run out of material. Mush on!

Mike Peters

3

5

THE DEMISE OF
THE TUSK FAIRY...

12

13

15

16

17

19

21

© Tundra 1993

CHAD...DUDLEY AND I HAVE A FEW COMPLAINTS...

YES?

...WE FEEL WE'RE BEING TAKEN ADVANTAGE OF... I MEAN THINK ABOUT IT... WE'RE THE **BACKBONE** OF THIS STRIP, THE **STARS**...

...BUT <u>YOU'RE</u> ALWAYS THE ONE THAT GETS THE **T.V. INTERVIEWS**, THE **FAST CARS**, THE **FABULOUS WOMEN!** AND FOR WHAT!?! WHAT SORT OF CONTRIBUTION DO **YOU** MAKE...?

Chad Carpenter...

I DRAW YOU...

WELL NO MORE FREE RIDE BUSTER!

© Tundra 1993

UH...SHERM..., I KNOW **BOYCOTTS** AND **STRIKES** ARE ALL THE RAGE NOWADAYS... BUT ISN'T THIS **RISKY**?

TUNDRA UNFAIR TO IMAGINARY CARTOON ANIMALS

JUST SAY **NO** TO TUNDRA

I MEAN, WHAT HAPPENS IF CHAD DECIDES HE DOESN'T NEED US...? WHAT IF HE DECIDES TO **REPLACE** US...?

JUST SAY **NO** TO TUNDRA

REPLACE US!? HA! ONCE CHAD REALIZES HOW **IRREPLACABLE** WE ARE, HE'LL BE **BEGGING** TO MEET OUR DEMANDS...!

CARTOON ANIMALS

Chad Carpenter...

NEXT...!

TUNDRA INC.

HELP WANTED

23

25

27

31

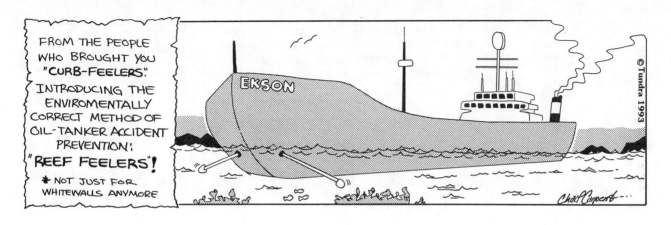

36

37

HELLO, AND WELCOME TO "THE PEOPLE'S PARKING COURT," I'M DOUG LLEW-ELLYN. THE LITIGANTS FROM OUR LATEST CASE ARE NOW LEAVING THE COURTROOM...

MR. CARPENTER... HAVING A BEAR AS YOUR LAWYER AND A PARKING METER AS YOUR WITNESS... HOW INCREDIBLY STUPID! I LAUGHED SO HARD I ALMOST CHOKED...

CHOKE, EH? I'VE GOT SOMETHING FOR YOU TO CHOKE ON...!

UH-OH

SORRY MR. LLEWELLYN, BUT YOUR METER SEEMS TO HAVE EXPIRED...

BEEP BEEP

CHINK

GAG ACK

SO, I HEAR DUDLEY MADE A **TOTAL FOOL** OF YOU IN TRAFFIC COURT TODAY...

YEP.

DO YOU THINK THIS WILL HAVE A DAMAGING AFFECT ON HIS CAREER AS AN ATTORNEY?

I DON'T KNOW... LAST TIME I SAW HIM, HE WAS IN THE **MIDDLE** OF SOME IMPORTANT PAPERWORK...

C'MON CHAD! LET ME OUT! I TOLD YOU I WAS GONNA' GIVE YOU A **DISCOUNT** ON MY LEGAL FEES...!

39

40

WHERE IN THE BLUE BLAZES HAVE YOU BEEN, CHAD!? YOU WERE SUPPOSED TO PICK ME UP FOR MY DENTIST APPOINTMENT HOURS AGO!

IT...IT WAS **HORRIBLE**... ..."IT WAS **ENDLESS**... I...I WAS **TOTALLY HELPLESS**... AS IF I WERE TRAPPED IN SOME SORT OF EVIL **NIGHTMARE**...!

..."I DIDN'T THINK I'D EVER SEE MY FAMILY OR FRIENDS AGAIN...

WHAT!? WHAT!? WERE YOU **MUGGED? ROBBED? ATTACKED BY A BEAR!?**

I WAS STUCK BEHIND A **MOTORHOME** FOR THE PAST 2½ HOURS!!!

GOOD HEAVENS! THEY'RE COMING OUT OF HIBERNATION EARLY THIS YEAR...

HA HA! GET A LOAD OF THIS, DUDLEY... THE PRESIDENT OF THE LOCAL RV ORGANIZATION, "**THE SON OF GOOD SAM CLUB**", SAYS THAT YESTERDAY'S **TUNDRA** STRIP ABOUT SLOW MOTORHOMES WAS **OFFENSIVE**...

..."HE'S ACCUSING ME OF **BLASPHEME**, AND WARNING ME TO SLEEP WITH ONE EYE OPEN... NOT ONLY THAT, BUT HE'S ALSO OFFERING A **REWARD** FOR MY HEAD — **DEAD OR ALIVE**... **HA! HA!**

CHOONK!

OOOSSSSH

WHOOM

I'LL BET SALMAN RUSHDIE COULD USE A ROOMMATE...

41

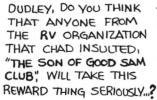

DUDLEY, DO YOU THINK THAT ANYONE FROM THE RV ORGANIZATION THAT CHAD INSULTED, "THE SON OF GOOD SAM CLUB", WILL TAKE THIS REWARD THING SERIOUSLY...?

KILL THE HERETIC!!

AAAAA!

OFF WITH THE INFIDEL'S HEAD...!

Chad Carpent...

YOU WERE SAYING...?

NEVER MIND.

PSST... DUDLEY...

UH... HOWDY STRANGER.

DUDLEY, IT'S ME... CHAD...

WHAT ARE YOU DOING IN THOSE BUSHES...?

EVER SINCE I TICKED OFF THAT RV GROUP, "THE SON OF GOOD SAM CLUB", I'VE HAD TO GO INTO HIDING...

...I'M CONSTANTLY LOOKING OVER MY SHOULDER, THINKING ONE OF 'EM IS ABOUT TO "WHACK" ME...

...AND WITH THAT REWARD OUT ON ME, I CAN'T TRUST ANYONE...

ABOUT THAT REWARD, CHAD... HOW MUCH IS IT...?

Chad Carpent...

42

43

44

47

49

53

55

56

59

60

63

I CAN'T BELIEVE I JOINED A **CRIME SYNDICATE** THINKING IT WAS A CARTOON SYNDICATE... **! I'VE GOT TO QUIT...!**

I'M NO EXPERT... BUT I THINK ONCE YOU JOIN AN ORGANIZATION SUCH AS THIS, YOU'RE IN IT FOR **LIFE**...

© Tundra 1993

O.K. THEN, I WON'T QUIT! I'LL **RETIRE**! THEY **CAN'T** GET MAD AT A GUY FOR **RETIRING**!

I WONDER WHAT KIND OF **RETIREMENT PACKAGE** THEY OFFER...

A MAHOGANY ONE, WITH BRASS HANDLES...

UH, MR. ZAMBONI... COULD WE HAVE A WORD WITH YOU...?

COME IN.

...UH... WE WEREN'T AWARE WHEN WE SIGNED ON WITH YOUR SYNDICATE THAT IT WAS A... ER... **CRIME** SYNDICATE... HE HE...

SILLY US...

© Tundra 1993

YOU SEE, I'M A **CARTOONIST**... WE THOUGHT THIS WAS A **CARTOON** SYNDICATE... UH... I'M SURE THIS HAPPENS ALL THE TIME... HE HE...

YEAH, ALL THE TIME... HE HE

I GET IT... YOU WANT MORE MONEY TO "WHACK" PEOPLE... IS THAT IT...?

NO NO NO

HANG ON, CHAD... LET THE MAN TALK...

67

69

71

74

75

77

79

82

85

87

88

89

THE DANGERS OF "MUSKRAT LOVE"

93

95

97

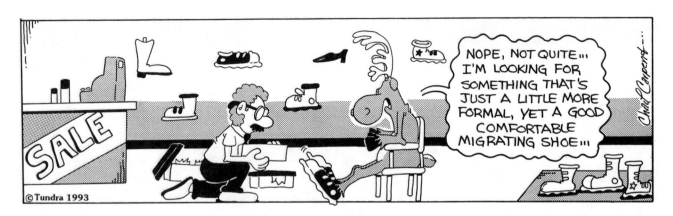

101

103

106

107

108

111

115

117

About the Cartoonist...

Found in a baleen basket floating in the Bering Sea, the infant Chad was rescued by a group of Eskimos who were returning from a whale hunt. Chad quickly learned the art of doodling, often staying up all night by the light of a seal oil lamp. Although his drawing talent was quite impressive, his hunter-gatherer talents were quite pathetic. So one day, in the pursuit of making a living which wouldn't involve walrus entrails, young Chad struck out into the world to find fame and fortune as a cartoonist.

Chad, friend to all woodland creatures, seen here contributing to nature's delicate food chain ...